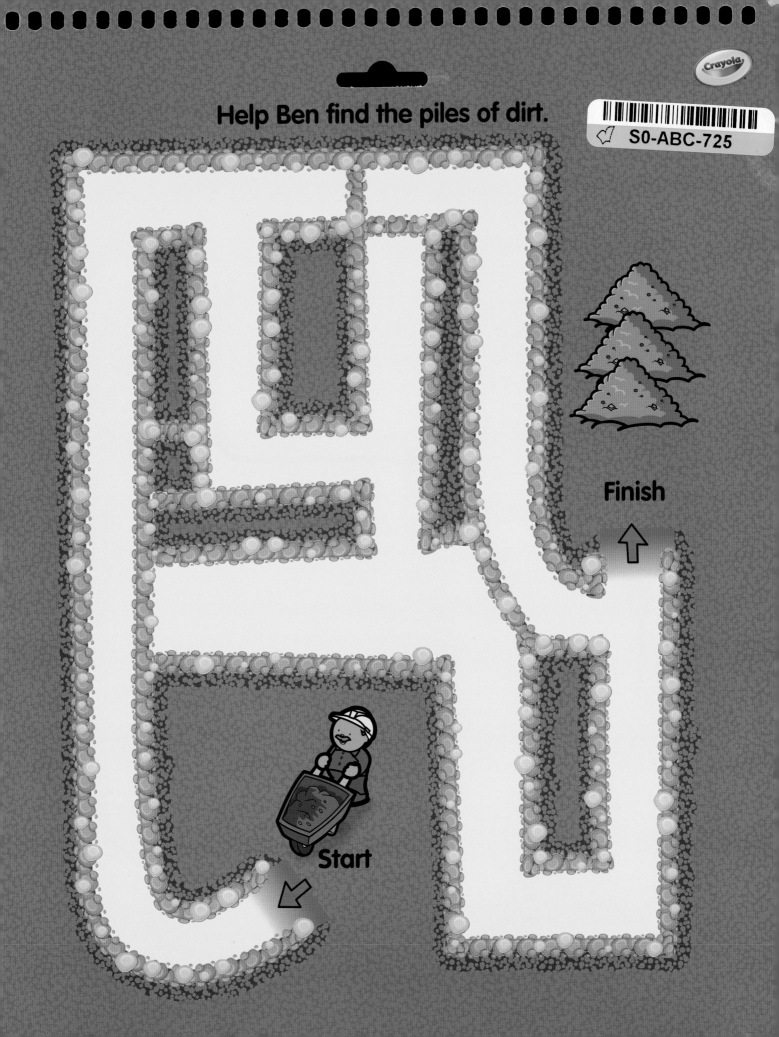

Help Ben find the piles of dirt.

Help the dump truck get to the hole.

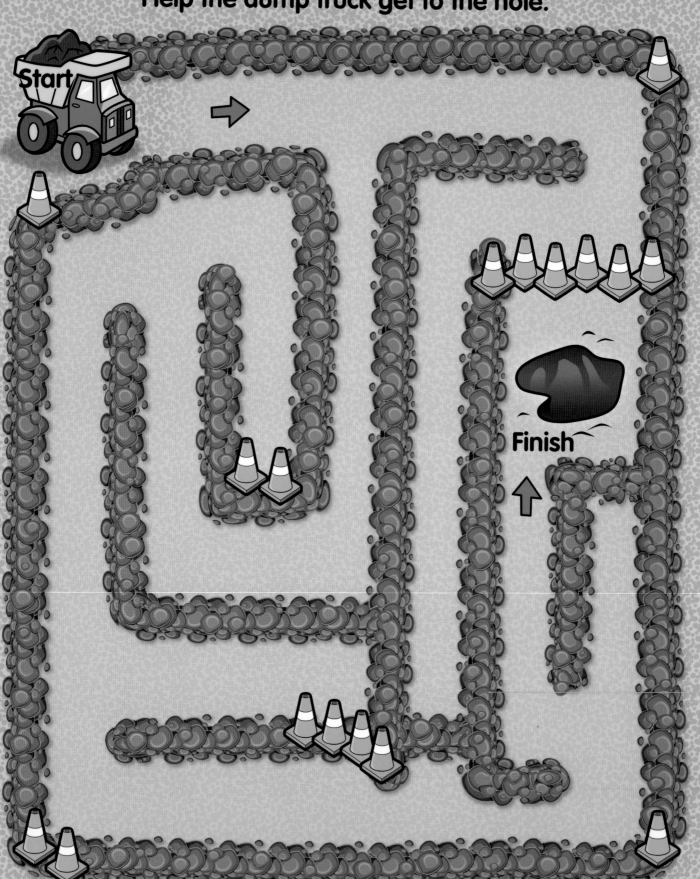

Start

Finish

Connect the dots from **1** to **20**. What is it?

Drive the bulldozer through the maze to the piles of gravel.

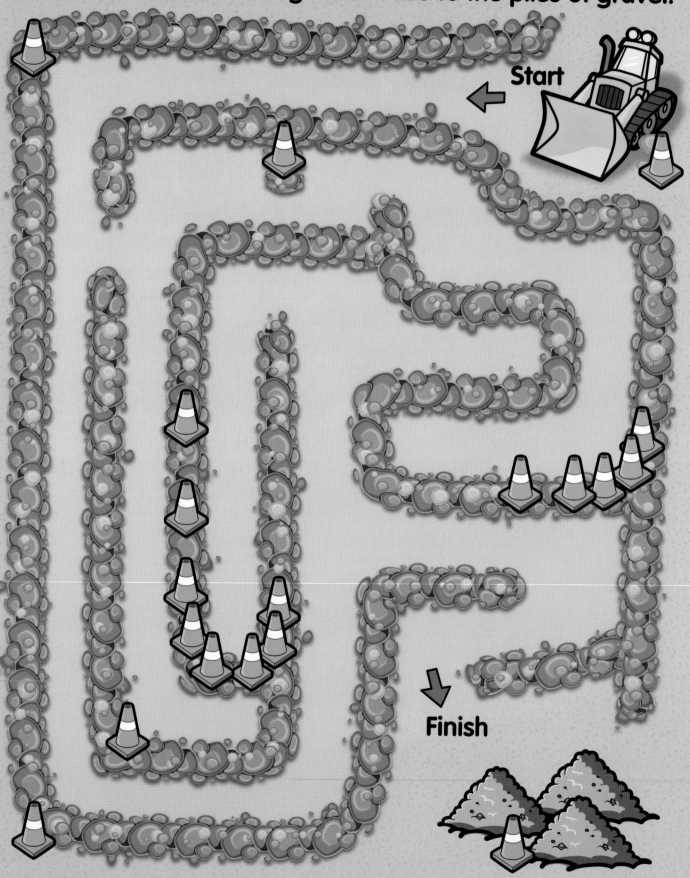

Start

Finish

Draw pictures of the six construction words you see below.

NAILS   HAMMER   DRILL

SAW   BUCKET   LEVEL

Get the crane to the beams by finding a way through the maze.

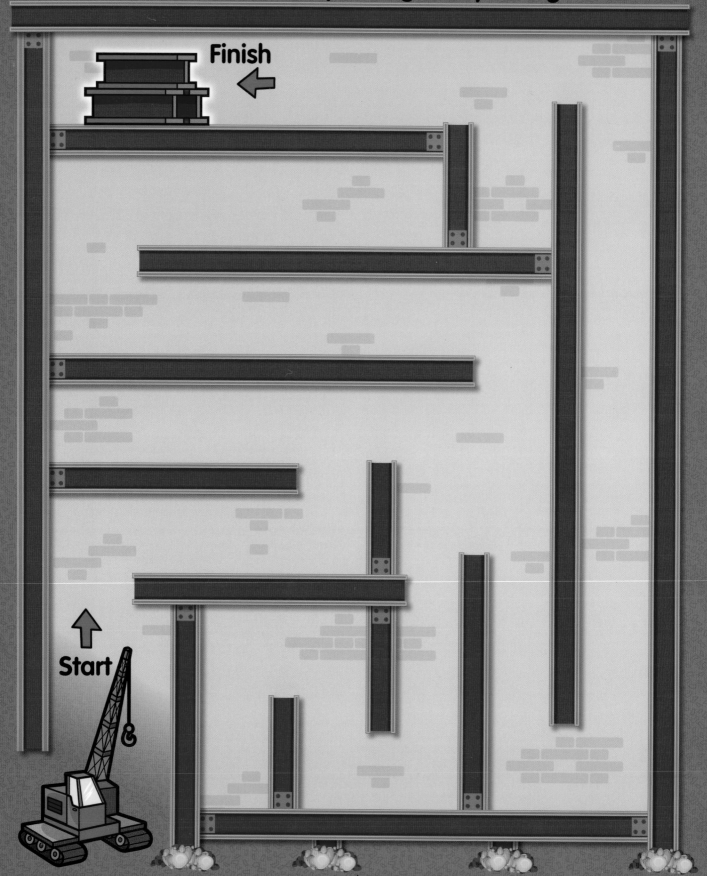

Finish

Start

Help Patty find her way out of the rope maze.

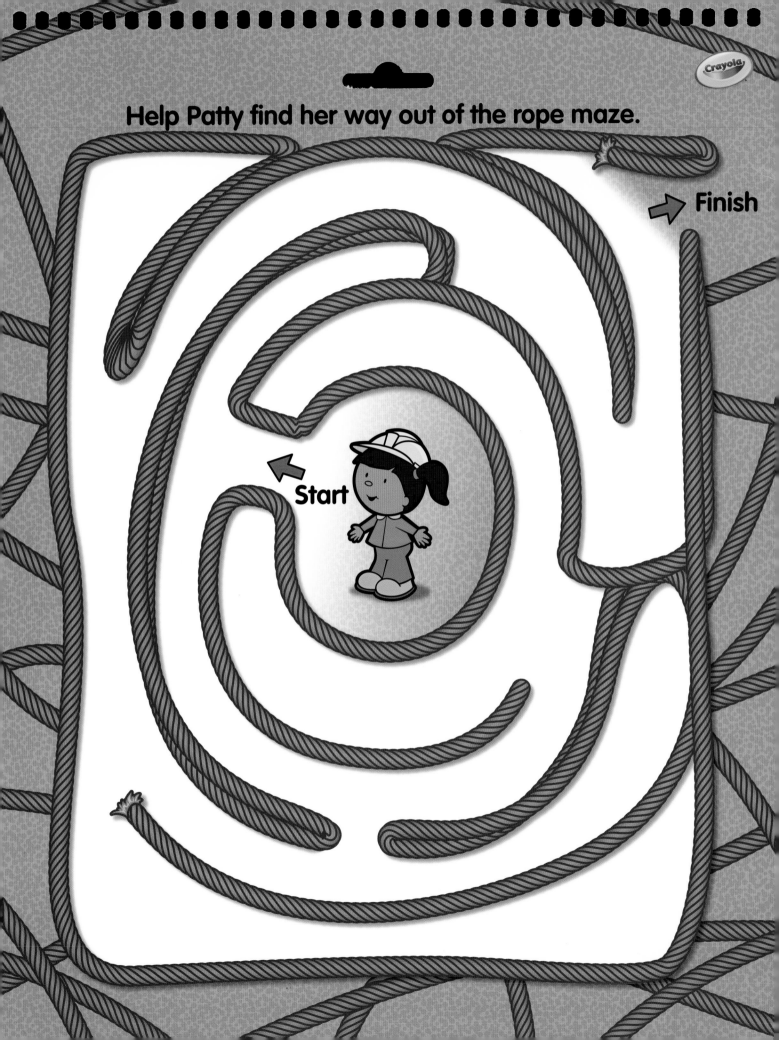

Finish

Start

Tyson needs his wrench. Help him through the maze.

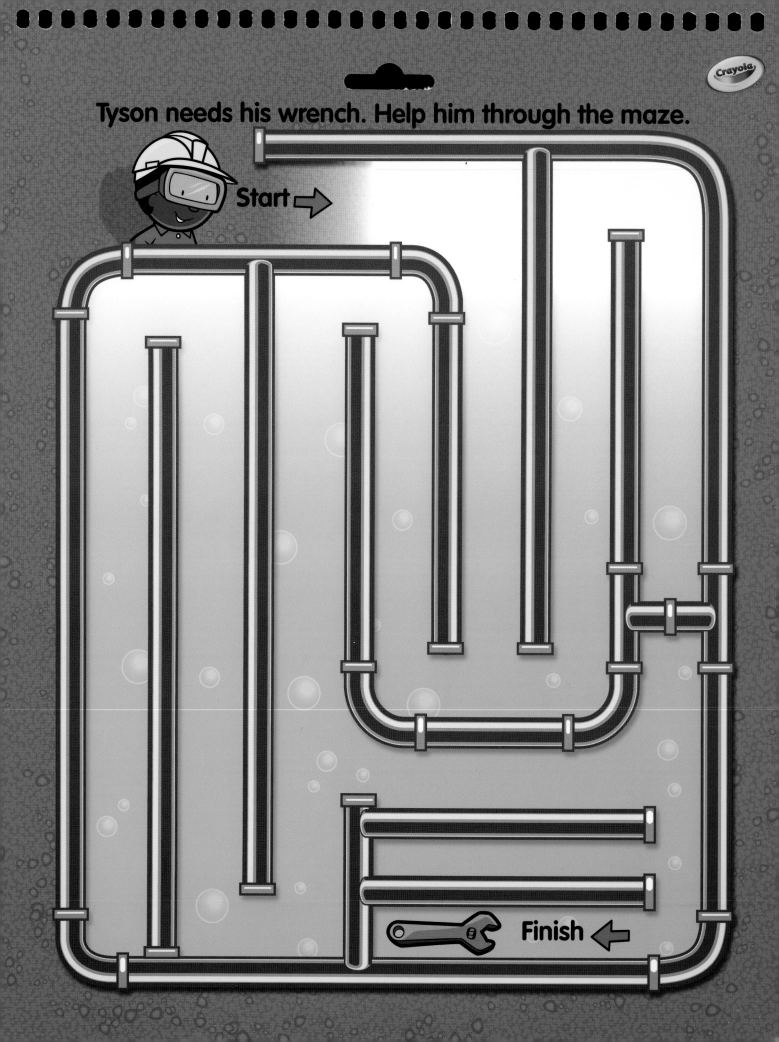

Draw lines to match the objects that go together.

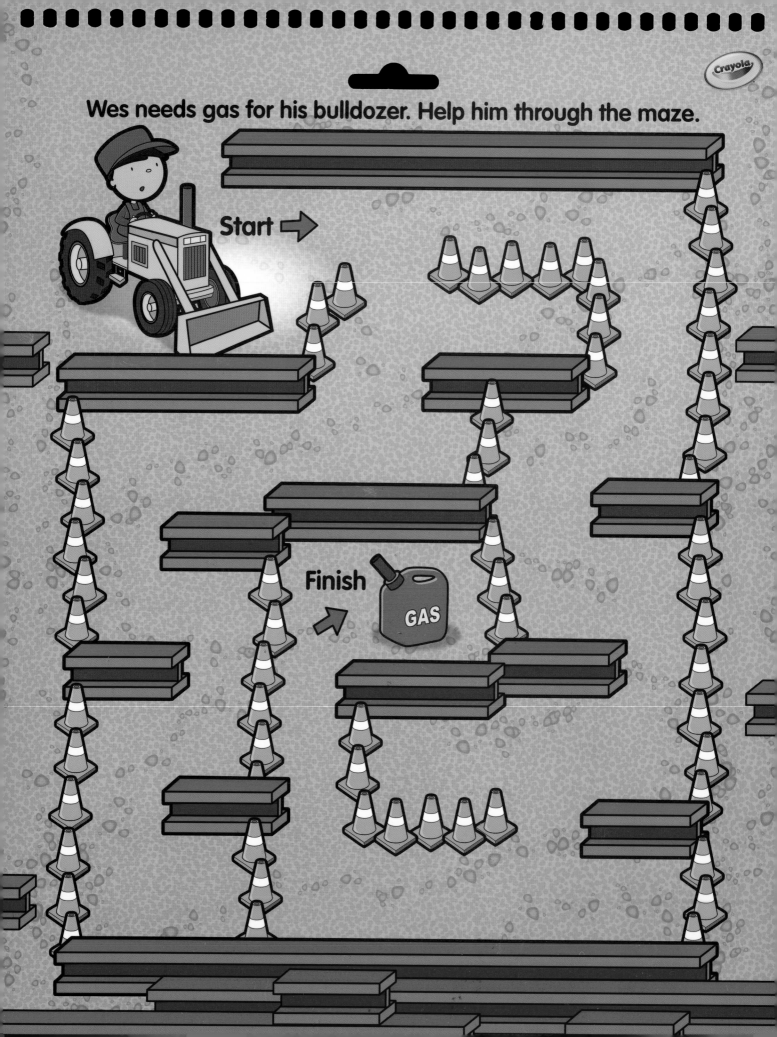

Help Mia get to the planks at the end of the maze.

Start

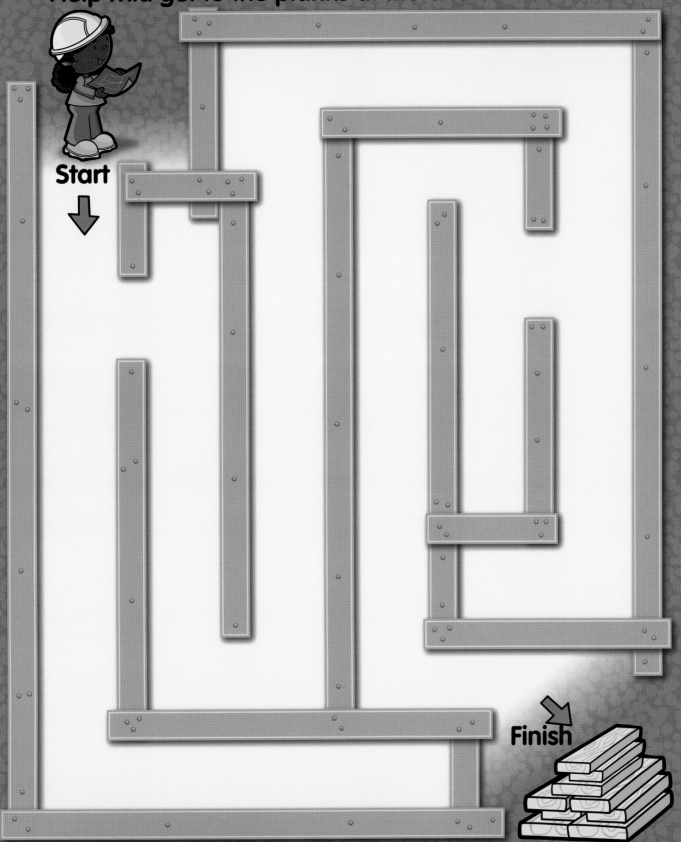

Finish

Help Leo find his saw. Draw a picture of something Leo might build.

Finish

Start